finally is set free to continue its journey back to the continental shelf where the gannets spend the summers, fishing and living upon the waters of the north. This completes the annual cycle of the bird's life, the pattern it will follow for the remainder of its years.

The interesting point about this sensitive story, told with compassion and understanding, is that it sets straight a general misconception. To the average person, the life of a bird such as the one written about, is one of routine, whereas in reality this bird must battle to survive, takes part in great adventures such as the migratory flights south and north, and faces dangers from many directions. A man has many score years in which to experience the fullness of life; but a bird crams just as much living into a very short time. The wonder of it all is that so many survive to live out their years.

The Straggler is a change-of-pace book for Ester Wier who has won a wide and devoted audience for her books for young people of which *The Loner* was a Newbery Medal runner-up. Mrs. Wier lives in Satellite Beach, Florida.

THE STRAGGLER

THE
STRAGGLER

ADVENTURES OF A SEA BIRD

by ESTER WIER

ILLUSTRATED BY LEONARD VOSBURGH

DAVID McKAY COMPANY, Inc.   NEW YORK

J

THE STRAGGLER

Typography by Charles M. Todd

To Rose Dobbs
who encouraged and inspired
this book

THE STRAGGLER

ONE

SPRING had arrived ahead of time in the cold
north country and now, in mid-March, the
birds were beginning to return from their winter
travels to southern regions. High on a bleak cliff
on one of the islands lying to the east of the province
of Quebec, a female gannet, known also as a sea
goose, waited. Overcome by a feverish impatience,
she had left the warmer climate early, heading
north to the same nesting grounds from which she
had departed six months before as a prebreeder.
Now her time had come. Now she would find a
mate, and together they would build a nest.

Far below, the breakers crashed against boulders,
sending a smoky spray high into the air. Slowly the

1

stored warmth of the sun, held deep under the waters, would start to rise and in another month the sea would begin to catch up with the seasonal changes of the land.

The bird had not left her post since arrival, able for the time to live without food or drink. Soon the air would fill with a blizzard of great birds coming home from their far winter journeys and she must be there when that happened. Twice as large as herring gulls, web-footed and short-legged, their heads touched with gold, their body plumage white and their wings black-tipped, the gannets would wheel and swoop, glide and hover as they came in to the nesting grounds. It was then she would call one down, and with him perform the rites of the marriage ceremony.

Three hundred feet above the sea, the harsh cliff towered at the eastern rim of the island. Here on the summit the earth was rocky and barren and windswept. As it leveled off and then sloped gently downward, it merged with grassy meadows where horned larks and water pipits made their nests. On beyond were fir and spruce trees, edged by a thin border of white birch.

Watching upon the spire now, the sea goose at last saw to the south a line of birds flying just above

the water. Upon nearing the bluff, the leader caught the wind as it rose to climb the height and the rest followed, carried up on the ascending current.

The waiting female stretched her neck as high as possible and remained motionless, silent. Almost at once a male of the flock wheeled and dipped, then dropped to a landing near her and, with extended neck, came closer until their breast feathers touched. With wings half-opened, the two raised their bills to the sky, clashing them together with a rattling sound as they fenced. Then, their greeting becoming vocal, they uttered harsh barking sounds, loud "urrah" notes before preening each other's throat feathers.

The formal wedding ceremony continued as the two bowed and curtsied to each other, pronouncing their cries again and again as they raised and lowered their heads, rocked back and forth, half-folded their wings and closed their tails, twisted and turned.

Once their vows were completed, the male set about choosing that certain portion of earth to be entirely theirs as long as they needed it, the nesting site. Many things had to be considered. If he picked a spot too near the cliff's edge or upon the rocky shelves on its face, the choice would offer more danger than advantage for while such locations allowed easy take-off, they also exposed the nest to winds strong enough at times to blow it and the young into the sea below. To settle too far from the brink, where the earth was level, would create a problem in leaving and returning to the gannetry since taking wing from flat land often proved impossible on a calm day for birds of their size.

The male made the wise decision, to build the nest mound just a little way from the bluff's threshold, within waddling distance of the edge for soon the entire area would become a living blanket of nesters and, surrounded by others, their young would be better protected from raiding gulls and robbing skuas. The space at the very rim of the colony would soon be occupied by prebreeders. After spending their first three years at sea, these junior birds were allowed to return and take up positions there in order to guard the fringe of the settlement as well as to learn by watching the routines of incubating and hatching. In full adult plumage now, they would be ready to mate in another year or so.

Once the male had decided upon the spot, he led his bride to it and began placing pellets of mud at her feet. These would form the foundation of the nesting mound they would build together. Back and forth he moved, carrying more marbles of earth while she worked them into shape with her webbed feet.

Day after day the couple continued their labors until the base for the mound was finished. Then the male departed on short trips to collect seaweed and whatever odds and ends he could find in the surrounding area. Announcing his return with a loud "urrah," he would assist his mate in fitting the treasure into the structure now taking shape before going off again to hunt another prize and bring it back.

The female stayed behind to guard the growing nest for there was always a chance of its materials being "borrowed" by the neighbors. The ground about was fast becoming covered with mounds as, daily, more and more birds arrived and settled. To a far-off observer, the cliff would have appeared to be covered by snow, while in the sky above the constantly hovering birds seemed to form a canopy of snowflakes which hung suspended in midair.

The thousands of nest mounds occupying the region permitted each pair only a few feet as its own, yet this small space was jealously guarded. One day, when the nest was nearing its planned height of one foot, and just before the hollow in which the egg would rest was to be scooped out at its top, the couple's territory was invaded.

Day by day gannets had gone about the business of building the mound or sitting upon the closely spaced nests. With choice spots fully occupied, new arrivals were forced to settle for either a niche on the bluff's rocky face or set up housekeeping on the sloping terrain now filled almost to overflowing. A first year breeder here, bound on a seaweed collecting mission, leaped suddenly into the air and beat his wings wildly. Lacking a handy cliff from which to fling himself or a path leading to one which did not run through unfriendly neighborhoods, the young bird did his best to become airborne. Almost at once, however, he crashed, knocking over several of the sea geese nearby. These immediately pecked at him viciously and, to avoid them, he hurled himself into the air once more and this time made just enough progress to carry him into the realm of the two who were busily occupied in adding the finishing touches to their nest.

Wings flailing, the trespasser landed, again laying low all surrounding nesters. Upon regaining balance, the male of the pair at once stepped forward to protect his territory. Belligerent, he seized the intruder's bill with his own and wrestled him to the ground while his mate did her part by attacking whatever portion of the stranger presented itself, and by pulling at tailfeathers within reach. The two battlers rolled about, first one on top, then the other, until the younger bird managed to free himself and escape. Covered with lumps marking the spots where he had been severely pecked, he made a rush for the cliff's edge. Half-running, half-flying, he had to pass other nesters on his way and they too stretched their necks to jab at him with their bills and add fresh wounds to those he already carried.

At last the nest was finished and for several days the pair took turns sitting upon it in order to raise its temperature by the warmth of their bodies. April had come and still birds flew in, riding the air as swimmers upon a current of water. Completing journeys of thousands of miles, they swept in from the open sea to crowd onto every foot of earth, all the way back to the meadows.

Finally the egg "arrived," a pale blue-green, covered with a chalky-white coating and just the right size for the parent who was sitting upon the nest at the time to cover with one webbed foot and overlap that with the other. For a month and a half now the pair would brood, one sitting while the other flew to sea to bathe and feed. Each would turn or adjust the egg several times an hour, warm it, and guard it from any other living creature that might attempt to draw near.

Most of the time the two worked together, each doing his part in the daily routine, but now and then when, after the usual greeting of stretching necks, raising wings, and uttering hoarse notes, the off-duty bird attempted to take over the next shift, the setting gannet might become balky and refuse to give up the nest until pushed or prodded off. Displaced, it would then waddle away, to return shortly with an offering in its bill, a piece of seaweed or a few feathers. These were presented to the sitter who usually grasped the material firmly and started a tug of war. Back and forth they would pull it until, growing weary of the play, they finally tucked it into the mound together and the sea-bound bird departed.

Marching to the edge of the cliff, it bounded into the air and took off. In one such leap, the creature passed from a ridiculously awkward stumbling clown on the land to a sublimely soaring master of the air. Flying close to the surface of the water, the bird would suddenly dive into a wave, pop up to the surface almost immediately, and then bathe again and again before heading for open water where it would spend the next few hours hunting the herring and codlings feeding upon plankton in the spring sea.

Though the bird colony was always in a riotous confusion of comings and goings, nest buildings and hatchings, feedings and bickerings over territorial claims, it was a fairly peaceful and safe haven since the predators threatening it were commonly of the winged kind. The bright-eyed and alert herring gull and the hawklike skua were always hanging about, awaiting an opportunity to rob unguarded nests of egg or chick, and these the gannets recognized and defended against by constant watchfulness. What they feared most was the eagle, that great white-tailed ruler of the sky whose hunger must be satisfied by small birds and mammals when fish grew scarce.

Following a storm, there appeared above the gannetry in the morning one of these enemies, either blown off course by the night wind, or come in search of food. The huge, broad-winged bird was discovered as soon as it became visible, its presence sending the nesters into panic on the ground below. Soaring in circles, now and then uttering its cry of "gak-gak-gak-gak" as it flew over the colony, it stretched its neck and opened its beak wide. With penetrating gaze, it examined the area below it in detail. Able to pinpoint a target with the exactness of a bomb-sight, it hovered before stooping on its prey.

Alarm swept the settlement on the island. Gannets rushed to and fro, crashing into each other, screaming their loud "urrah." Those not sitting on eggs leaped from the cliff's rim and soon there was a deafening roar of wings from thousands in the air. Forming a great turbulent cloud above their colony, the birds hung there, creating such disorder and chaos that finally the eagle, no longer able to see his chosen victim because of the feathered snowstorm below him, gave up and flew on to search out other sea cliffs and other prey.

TWO

THE young nestling, though blind and naked at birth, was a miracle of design. His heart was large and its beat strong and rapid. His body temperature was high and air sacs lay just beneath his skin as cushions against the shock of striking the water in those steep dives he would make someday. His feathers, when they appeared, would be light yet durable and strong, forming an insulation to trap air and support him when floating. His eyes would be equipped with a wonderful extra eyelid to protect them in both the air and the water, and his webbed feet would act as propellers to move him under the sea as he chased his food, just as his streamlined body would speed his passage through the air. Narrow wings and a pointed tail would lift him into flight and keep him airborne whether soaring in the heights or gliding close to the ocean's surface.

His skin was dark, his bill, legs and feet gray. Devoted parents smoothed out his feathers regularly and he responded to their attentions with faint chirping sounds. They fed him a semi-liquid diet at first but soon they would begin to stuff him with enormous amounts of solid food so that when they left him on his own, he would be able to live on his fat for a while.

Within a few days the beginnings of pale, creamy-white down could be seen on his body and at eight days his eyes opened. As he grew, his hunger grew also, and he began to beg with a series of rapid sounds. In his eagerness to fill his belly, he would even thrust his head down his parents' throats after food, never ceasing to "uk-uk-uk" all the while.

At three weeks, the chick was entirely covered with a yellowish down and the feathers upon his wings had begun to sprout. Each of these was shaped to perform a special task in flying so that someday, when his flight plumage was complete, he too would be able to hurl himself from cliffs and climb to sweep the sky in great widening circles.

As he grew stronger, he began to take an interest in his surroundings, rearranging the nesting material, removing a piece here, tucking it back into place there, or refusing to give it up when one of his parents tugged at the other end of it. Nests all around were now occupied with young, and the air of the gannetry was filled with faint chirpings, with begging calls, and the "ugh-ugh-ugh" of the chicks old enough to walk about and visit other nests.

As his senses developed, the chick became aware of a great deal that went on in the colony. Standing on tiptoe, he would flap his small wings when a non-nesting bird strayed into the territory of the cliffside dwellers and was immediately challenged. Once he watched as two birds, barking loudly, became locked in a furious tussle and rolled too near the edge of the rise, disappearing at last to crash onto the sharp rocks below.

Tragedy would come in other forms too, and this he learned one afternoon when the sun shone and puffs of white cotton clouds drifted lazily overhead. The size of each family's territory was limited by custom, its nest being so placed that the bird sitting upon it was in the very center of the plot and could not quite reach its neighbor, even by stretching its neck and thrusting out its bill.

The young gannet, being preened by his mother, watched as two nearby parents strayed momentarily from their nests, one leaving an egg exposed to the warm sunshine, the other a hatchling. Although they were only a waddle or two away from home, a herring gull swept in with a flurry of long slender wings, pecked open the egg and swallowed its contents, then seized the tiny chick from the other nest and gulped it down. With a loud croaking call, it was gone before the parent gannets could protest. Flying back to its own nest of seaweed on a nearby cliff, it alighted and settled down to preen itself.

Though this was the young bird's first experience with a predator, he had recognized at once that it was an enemy. After that, he grew extremely cautious and many times during a day would take fright at any sudden movement near him.

When he was old enough to leave the nest and walk about the colony, still clad in his wooly down, he found there were certain perils he must face alone. Adult birds were apt to threaten when he trespassed upon their square of ground. A male might even advance with open beak, making a scooping motion which the chick discovered brought forth an instinctive reaction in himself so that he bowed his head and tucked his bill into his breast, leaving his neck exposed to the belligerent in an act of surrender. Settling down right where he was, close to the ground, he would remain motionless. The action seemed to work for he was never harmed during such encounters.

It did not work, however, when he met others his own age. When young chicks attacked each other, it was with open beaks outthrust, and loud quacking calls repeated over and over. No amount of bowing or settling to the ground then could save the weaker one from peck lumps on its head and body.

Flight feathers began to show as he gradually traded his fluff for a dark coat with patchy light markings. His bill turned brown and his eyes a grayish blue, and day by day he grew fatter, fed and cared for by attentive parents. Yet all the protection they offered could not spare him his first real fright, an experience with the most terrifying predator of all, man!

A week earlier there had been a change in the weather, with warm sunshine giving way to a blanket of fog which rolled across the sea from the outer banks, washing the rocky cliffs in a smothering and persistent mist. The faint warning sound of bells ringing upon shallows and banks and reefs drifted in from far away, and the mournful voice of fog-horns haunted the days and the nights. The sea birds knew their way through the fog and all day gannets filled the air, appearing out of nowhere to relieve their mates on nest duty or taking off into a gloom as gray and pale as the waters below.

On the seventh day a wind came up and the fog began to thin. It was then that the gannetry was disturbed by sounds so unusual that a number of birds, growing uneasy, erupted into flight and hung over the area, waiting.

The young bird was on a walking and visiting expedition at the time. He sensed the change and watched, curiously, as the prebreeders just beyond, at the fringe of the settlement, grouped to stand their ground and guard against what might come. Joined by birds which had not mated that year, they all prepared to face the intruders whose voices now were coming closer.

Even had the chick seen the men pull the boat up on the surf-washed small beach at the foot of the bluff, he would not have understood the kind of danger they represented, yet sensing somehow that along with the others he also was imperiled, he hugged the ground and remained motionless in the attitude of surrender which had so often protected him in the past.

"Hey, Mike, maybe we better not. Ain't it against the law? Ain't they likely to fight back?" The words came from one of the climbers on the long unused path which zigged and zagged up the cliff's steep face.

"We need bait, don't we, kid?" the other replied. "Anyhow, who's to see us in this fog? Who's to know? No use worryin' 'bout them fightin' back. We can take 'em easy. I was here once before, long time ago. Anyway, far as these blasted birds is concerned, it'll serve 'em right. They eat our cod so now we put 'em on our cod hooks. Got your oar? Just do as I do and we'll get it over with fast and get out of here."

Not even the appearance of the two men as they pulled themselves over the cliff edge drove the pre-breeders and nesting birds from their stations since to remain was the only defense they knew. Their necks were outstretched and their bills gaped. The chick, however, at the sight of the enemy rushed back to the haven of the nest, uttering sharp cries of alarm all the way there.

"Wow!" the boy cried in amazement at the white cover of nesting birds spread out before him as far as he could see. "They good to eat? There's enough here to feed an army."

The man lifted his oar above his head. "Uh, uh," he grunted. "Tough and oily. Young ones might be I guess but the bigger they are, the more bait they'll make."

Afterwards, the men left by climbing over the edge and down the twisting path, loaded with their booty. Only because of the number of prebreeders that had remained on guard were the nearby nests undisturbed and the young gannets' lives spared.

A cover of white birds hovered in silence over the heads of the raiders and when the men reached the beach below, it dropped even lower. All their gestures and waving of oars once they had dumped their kill into the skiff, did no good for as they rowed hurriedly back to the fishing boat, it accompanied them into the receding fog.

Now the young sea goose would add the shape and actions of another predator to that of the gull already engraved upon his awareness. From now on, man was to be counted among dangers he must avoid whenever possible.

Warm summer weather returned and the parents of the three-month-old gannet departed, flying off to sea together one morning, their job of caring for their young finished. The chick waited at the nest for days, living on his stored fat, finishing his growth, before joining a group of his fellow fledglings, clad in the same dark plumage he wore. Together they passed the next week, exercising their wings by flapping them vigorously, for the urge was upon them also to leave the nesting grounds. Open water far away was calling to them.

During that time hunger was a companion as they pitched and tossed and floundered back and forth upon the cliff's rim, working themselves up to that fateful moment when they must leap from their perch in a first wild attempt at flight. Not strong enough yet for sustained flying, they would hope to reach the water safely and then drift upon its surface for a time, until their muscles hardened and they learned to feed themselves. Only then would they be ready to head for the continental shelf where the deep ocean began.

The first to leave tottered upon the edge and, half-flying, half-falling, sideslipped into a crash landing upon the sea. Almost immediately another followed, stretching his wings, flaring his pointed tail, only to be pushed into space by a sudden wind gust and to fall leadenly upon the rocks below. Now the young fledgling, his short legs and webbed feet stoutly supporting him, stretched his neck and aimed his bill at the sky. Peering down, his eyes swiveled inward to look from under his bill at the spray below, rising like smoke. Far, far down there, he could see the chick which had leaped first, bobbing as it rode upon the water.

He raised his wings over his back as he had seen the parent birds do. Turning from side to side, pausing, then extending his wings and beating them violently, he at last launched himself into the air. However, instead of rising he began to fall, powerless to control his movements. More thrashing managed to slow his descent and, luckily, he was caught in a rising current of air. After taking him aloft, it sent him coasting downhill, all the way to the water where he crashed into a large swell, bobbing to the surface again in a second or two. Feeling himself pulled shoreward by a breaker, he used all his strength to turn himself about and begin paddling awkwardly in the opposite direction.

Now he was a sea bird! Now his home was no longer the land but the boundless sea stretching there before him.

THREE

THE young gannet drifted upon the tides, farther and farther from the island. His main need was food but his first awkward attempts at getting it were unsuccessful.

Gulls mewed and squealed, yelped and "laughed" all about him. Landing upon the water, they fed on small fish near the surface or followed fishing boats to fight over refuse. Where fish were thick, they seemed to fill the sky, always noisy, always hungry.

Once he floated near a skiff and the lone fisherman tossed a crust of bread to him. Quickly grasping and swallowing it before a gull could snatch it, he paddled away frantically, having recognized this was his enemy, man. His first good fortune came when he rode the water's flow into a yellow-brown ribbon of plankton. Here were the riches of the sea meadows, millions of tiny floating animals and plants. Here were small crabs, worms, the fingerling of many fish, and the young gannet ate hungrily and heartily, moving along with the pasture for days. When the wandering currents finally carried the blanket of plankton beyond him, he was stronger and now began to fish with confidence.

He learned that his throat could expand to receive a large-sized catch, that when rain came down like a gray curtain about him he could not see to fish, that mackerel and herring when feeding upon the surface betrayed themselves by a noise like rain falling upon the water. He discovered too that, except for the rackety gulls and the shrill wind, the ocean was a silent place, unlike the turmoil and clamor of the nesting area. Here the adult gannets, pausing briefly on their way to the rich fishing grounds of the continental shelf, to plunge headlong into the water after schooling menhaden, did so without uttering the loud, hoarse, barking cries they used on land at every occasion. His own sight and hearing sharpened and what he did not seem to know by instinct, he learned by observation. Now, as he floated high upon

the waters, he gaped and shook his head as the breeders did, and rested quietly for a time after a successful catch, in order to finish swallowing his meal.

During his third week of independence, he reached an area out of sight of land, and here he found three of his fellow fledglings, none of whom had yet attempted to try his wings for a second time although all exercised regularly, flapping and stretching as they drifted. Until they were more certain how to use winds and waves for their own benefit, they would continue their life of floating and growing.

The four stayed together, fishing by day, sleeping by night, and at times paddling their webbed feet in order to prevent themselves from being carried apart by the swift-running tides.

One day the sea goose made an especially good catch, an eight-inch glistening herring. In preparing to give all his attention to swallowing it, he failed to note the arrival of a skua in the sky above. Resembling a brown gull, the large bird wheeled about on spotting the silver gleam of the catch and now, with wings moving agilely in deep fast strokes, dropped to a landing. Sharp talons and hooked bill had earned it a reputation as a sea bandit. Of a fighting nature, fearless and strong, it lived by robbing other birds of food, even forcing them to regurgitate the prey they had already swallowed.

When close above, it gave voice to a wild screeching shriek and was upon the gannet at once. The struggle took only a moment. Overwhelmed, pinned down upon the water, the young bird readily parted with his prize. Never would he forget how the white patch on the brigand's wings flashed as it departed.

So excited was he by the attack that not only did he disgorge all the food he had eaten recently, but he also made a panicky attempt at take-off in order to leave the area as fast as possible. It was a calm day and even had he been experienced, he would have found it difficult to rise from the water. Now, with neck and tail outstretched, wings raised above his back, not all his efforts were able to move him skyward by so much as an inch.

On and on the four drifted, always toward the deep sea. When rain prevented their fishing or the harvest was slim, they accepted refuse from the fishing fleet, though none of them chose to go nearer than necessary for a handout. The sight of them caught the attention of men aboard one of the boats on a day when there was little action and the skies had turned leaden gray.

"Thieving gulls," one worker said. "What you don't give them, they take. Manage to get it one way or another. I've seen them snatch a bait right off a line, clean as a whistle. Even found one in a net once, eighty feet down. They eat more fish than I can catch."

"Those aren't gulls," his companion told him, leaning his elbows on the rail and staring at the birds. "They're gannets. Heard they're called sea geese too. Ones out there are the young of the season. Grown ones are white with black tips on their wings."

"Oh, them. The ones that look the same coming or going, pointed at both ends? Ones you look up at and swear they got a white cross on their undersides?"

"The same. Used to be folks believed they were spirits of drowned fishermen come back to watch over their families. Always have a funny feeling when I see them. Suppose it's true. . . . ?"

Summer was at its peak now. The weather was fair and the sea quiet. The small group of fledglings chose to delay testing their wings since the absence of wind reduced their chances of success. Breeding gannets weren't to be seen in the skies now, remaining at their homes on the cliff to spare themselves the difficulties of flight take-off from smooth and windless seas.

Soon the land would start to cool. Although the ocean, slower to warm in the spring, would lag behind in the coming of cold weather still weeks away, there were now the first stirrings of change in its life. Birds began to respond to the rhythm of the season and to the slowly decreasing hours of daylight. Before long, the fever of migration would be upon them, and the pathways of the skies would fill.

Summer's end would also find fish moving south, the shift in the winds exciting them to action and bringing many of the young from bays and inlets to join schools which moved like dark shadows under the surface of the water.

During these weeks, the young gannet's curiosity had been developing and now he strayed from the small group whenever he saw or heard something worth investigating. The popping noise of small fish feeding in late evening could disturb him and draw him away, as did also his first sight of tiny creatures which a ripple on the water brought to full eerie glow on warm summer nights. The brilliant blue sail of a Portuguese man-of-war beckoned him as did a school of porpoises, flashing in the sun as they leaped and frolicked while harvesting a pasture of menhaden.

When puffy white clouds began to stack in the sky, and a wind sprang up from the south, the gannet sensed a coming weather change and once more sought his fellows, his restlessness giving way for the time to a flocking urge. Soon they would reach the shelf at the threshold of the deep. Here sea birds spent the days stirring the waters into a white froth as they plunged from stalls at dizzying heights down toward the spot where fish were thickest. Beyond the shelf, the floor of the ocean sloped to fall at last into dark and secret regions of gorges and canyons.

All that night, the sea geese rocked on the tossing waters, paddling in their sleep to keep from being swept apart with the tides. There was a ring around the moon and again the winds shifted. The calm, at last, was over. Toward morning, in the first gray hazy light, there was a disturbance which churned the sea until it foamed beneath one of the fledglings who immediately began thrashing his wings. Attempting to move away by beating the water with his free foot, he found that the large fish which had seized his other from below was too strong to shake off. In a moment he was gone, drawn under by the predator.

THE STRAGGLER

In panic the young gannet took off, neck and tail stretched out, wings flapping wildly. Now every ounce of energy he possessed was called upon, each feather strove to do its part, each newly toughened muscle went into action. Striving desperately, at last he succeeded in becoming airborne and, shifting his position, found himself sailing downwind, swiftly if unsteadily, upon a river of air. On and on he was carried, alternately flapping his wings stiffly and gliding. Once it moved him into a rising current which he climbed to where it became strong enough to support him, and then he started to soar, sweeping the sky in circles.

Had he known how, he would have headed toward the open sea. Instead, borne along with the wind drift, he covered a great tract of ocean and when, finally, he set himself down upon the waters, he was still many miles from his destination. That, however, did not matter. What was important was that he had tried his wings again. He could fly!

FOUR

IT took a few weeks for the young gannet to gain
confidence in flight. He learned that flying in
rough weather required little effort for by using the
force of wind thrown off the slope of wave and swell,
he was given the lift to move himself along. By seeking the channel between the waves, he found retreat
and shelter from the main windstream.

When, at last, he joined the colony of his fellows
at the edge of the trackless sea, he had already taught
himself to dive. Up, up, up, to fifty feet or more in
the air he would climb, and there he would glide
upon long narrow wings until he found a school of
fish and picked out his target. Then he would stall

for a moment in midair before half-folding his wings, pointing his head, raising his tail and launching himself on a steep downward plunge. Snapping his wings tightly against his body as he hit the water, he raised a fountain of white spray and, remembering the skua, often swallowed his catch before popping to the surface again. He learned to adjust the height of his dive to the depth at which his food swam and when the schools were just beneath the surface, he hung above them, darting after his prey, rather than falling upon it from above.

As time moved along, members of the colony began to depart and soon, instead of a sea whipped into froth by the mass of birds performing their splendid dives, there was less and less action just as there were fewer and fewer schools of fish. Drawn toward the south, both were starting on the long journey of migration.

Adult gannets from the nesting cliffs visited the shelf only briefly, then were gone, their departure as unannounced as their arrival had been. Swift kittiwakes passed by, dipping low over the waves, soaring high above the crests, settling for a few hours upon the waters with heads tucked under wings as they floated and rested. Thousands of tiny dovekies swept over with a roar of wings as they headed toward quarters on the open sea, and the pirates of the ocean, the skuas and jaegers, came to worry and vex the assembly before setting forth to roam the winter ocean.

The young gannet waited, drifting upon the night waters in sleep, feeding by day. He joined no group in diving and flying, choosing each day's companionship and destination according to his own fancy. As the southward pull grew stronger, the voices of night migrants grew loud in the sky, small birds using the cover of dark to pass unnoticed by their enemies. Daylight brought throngs of large, strong-winged birds, and changing winds brought strays pushed off their course. Above the distant land, a flood of birds streamed through the sky, gabbling and calling, hissing and chirping, in a great exodus from the bitter cold soon due in the north.

Then, finally, the day arrived when something within moved him to join a long airborne line of his own kind, on the greatest adventure of his young life. In the flock were a few mature breeders, large and white with black tips on wings which spread four to five feet, and creamy heads touched with gold. A greater number of the group were going south for their second winter, in changing plumage between early and late stages, patchy and mottled with streaks of white on their undersides and rumps. Those making up the majority were birds of the year, clad in dark feathers, standing out in contrast to their elders. They followed the experienced leaders on this, their first migration.

For these young, it was a flight into the unknown. Next spring they would be coming north again to a place they already knew, the fishing grounds at the shelf. After three years of such journeying, they would return at last to their birthplace, the gannetry on the cliffs, and settle at the edge of the nesting area as prebreeders.

Now the birds in the line flew close to the water, wings first flapping rapidly, then outstretched to sail and glide. No storms arose to blow them off their path, no fog hung in the air to confuse their navigation. They did not run into headwinds to slow their progress and weren't overtaken by tailwinds to upset their balance and ruffle their feathers.

They flew by day and slept on the waters at night after feeding upon swarms of herring or bronze and silver menhaden heading south also. Several times the young bird was tempted to veer off when they came close to land and a river mouth called or a bay opened its arms, but the flocking instinct and the southward pull proved stronger than his urge to stray.

Their first rest period of several days came when they reached waters off the coast of the United States. Here the warm stream from the south and the cold current from the north approached each other, carrying the riches of the sea to offer a temptingly choice menu to sea birds lingering to fuel themselves for the thousands of miles yet ahead of them. Moving shoreward, they found high cliffs rising a hundred feet or more above muddy tidal flats and here, at the water's edge, saw shore birds shuffling through seaweed and shells for tidbits and morsels of food.

All went well, the young gannet growing stronger and more experienced day by day. The first migrants had appeared in this area a month before, and the peak would not occur for another few weeks. By that time his flock would have reached warmer latitudes, with the older birds dropping off when the south coast was reached, the young ones continuing all the way to the waters of the Gulf of Mexico.

Of the millions of birds now on the move across land and sea, many would never reach their destination. Even while the gannets rested and fed off the rust-streaked bluffs where thousands of swallows made their homes, multitudes of birds were meeting death only a few hundred miles to the south.

A cold mass of air had swept in from the west and once it neared the coast had stopped. The skies thickened, rains came, and a host of small birds migrating by night flew lower to escape the troubled air above. Ahead of them the great white beacon of a light station searched the sky, and this brilliant ray first attracted, then blinded them, so that some flew straight up the beam to disaster while others, in confusion, beat themselves to death against the glass and steel of the building, dropping to the rocks below.

Seaward from that spot, low-lying clouds had forced other birds to climb above their usual path to where the air was thinner. Only as long as the bad weather persisted would they hold to this course, but it was long enough for a flock of golden plover, on their non-stop autumnal flight over the ocean, to plow into an airliner just beginning its descent for a landing at the terminal on the edge of a great city's harbor.

After the gannets had eaten their fill, they took up their journey again, rested and refreshed. Once more the weather had cleared, the air was warm, the sky an endless blue. Sometimes the leader of the

line would take a short detour to reach a cloud bank
formed by rising air currents which piled cotton
upon cotton until a great mass drifted lazily overhead. Just below there was sure to be a good updraft
and in it the entire company could rise in a bubble,
soaring higher and higher in the joyous freedom of
flight.

The next way station on their route was an island
whose long sandy fingers groped seaward. Here
again the sea geese would rest and feed in shoal
water while land birds, pausing also in flight, stuffed
themselves on sweet and juicy red-purple plums on
the beach, treading upon a carpet of pink mallow
spread over the sand.

Staying close to shore meant finding small squid
and shrimp, snail and copepod to dine upon for a
change and the flock would have lingered had it not
been for a crowd of people who appeared on the
usually deserted beach, laden with cameras, and bin-
oculars, pocket guides and spotting scopes. Quickly
the birds moved farther out to sea, preferring not to
remain within range of the humans.

The young gannet rose with the rest of his group
when the bird watchers came, taking to the air amid
the turmoil of flapping wings and loud hoarse bark-

ing "urrahs." The leader took them to safety out upon the swells, out of reach.

A buoy, crusted with mussels and barnacles, lifted and rolled and whistled in the gentle flow, and this at once claimed the attention of the curious young bird. He remained beside it all afternoon, feeding and resting. When dark fell and the flock settled for the night, drifting together on the slow-moving tide, he still did not join them but stayed where he was, in the comfort of the shelter he had found.

Just before dawn, three hungry killer whales, their tall fins cutting silently through the water, their mighty jaws armed with spikelike teeth, set sonars to work and zeroed in upon the birds. In an instant and without warning, the pack opened enormous throats and swallowed the flock whole, scarcely causing a ripple as they moved on to hunt more nourishment for their huge bodies.

FIVE

Now the bird was alone. He must continue his journey over a route he had never traveled before, toward a faraway place to which only an impulse was sending him. When lines of other migrants passed in the sky, he made no effort to join them for he would fly only with his own kind.

Fortunately, he was experienced. A strong flier, he had learned how to locate good feeding grounds and capture his fill of fish. He could recognize dangerous enemies and was skillful at finding his way without landmarks or even memory to direct him.

His greatest lack, perhaps, was his inability to forecast the weather ahead, never knowing what he might be flying into, fog or rain, strong wind or calm.

He was lucky at first, making good time over the sea. Food was plentiful, quartering breezes and mild tailwinds sped him along, and the cold weather which had moved over the north lands had been left far behind. But as he passed from temperate regions to those bordering on the tropics, his hollow bones felt a new pressure, exerted by the mass of air surrounding him. The moon had a halo about it, and the sun which was pale as it set, came up fiercely red in the morning sky.

A week before, far to the south and east, winds and squalls had met on an overheated patch of the sea and a storm had been born. Moving slowly west, it had grown in strength and had swept over a cluster of islands, doing great damage before turning north. As it came, it sucked winds from all directions into its core, like a whirlpool, and the bird, never swerving from his southward heading, was finally caught up along with hundreds of others and carried by strong currents into that heart. Here, in an area some twenty miles across, was a calm and for two days the gannet remained in warmth and quiet.

Ships, imprisoned also in the storm's eye, provided shelter for thousands of small travelers. Shrike,

warbler, and dove perched, dazed, upon chains and coils of line as they rested after being snatched up and tossed seaward by the great winds. The gannet kept his distance and drifted, resting and feeding himself.

Finally, the storm took another turn and headed toward land. Now he strove to stay where he belonged, in the pathway above the sea, but the revolving winds caught and carried him, trapped, up and up into the turbulence above. Streamlined, he pierced the air like an arrow flung through the sky, his call of panic lost in the swirling winds. Round and round he went, driven and beaten, buffeted and pummeled by forces too strong to fight, until at last he was flung aside, hundreds of miles at sea.

He made a vain effort to stay aloft even though he was spent and it was night. Beyond the storm's violence now, he still resisted dropping to the surface of the water since exhaustion might not permit him to stay afloat, might bring to him the same fate it had hundreds of birds he had seen earlier, lost in the sea below.

With his last ounce of strength, he fought to remain in the air but it was hopeless, and slowly he began losing altitude until suddenly, he brushed the mast of a ship and with a gargling cry of distress, dropped like a stone to the deck.

Rough hands seized him. "Glory be, it's raining birds!" a voice cried. Though the young sea goose knew this sound as that belonging to an enemy, he was too weary to struggle even when he felt himself lifted into the air.

"What do you think you're doing?" a second voice demanded.

"Throwing it back where it came from. It's only a sea gull."

Gentle hands took him, cradling his body as if it were precious. "I'll bet this bird comes from a place up near my home." The hands ran over his body, seeking, probing. "Got a badly bruised or broken wing. He's worn out too, and half-dead with fright. Must have been caught in that storm we've been dodging."

"Hey, maybe it's good to eat. Looks kind of like a goose. What you going to do with it?"

The man in whose hands he rested, talked to him in low soothing tones. "Going to fix you up, young fellow, if I can. Looks to me like you're awful young to be on your own way out here. You a straggler? You one of those who like being independent and doing things your own way? Me, too. Gets you into trouble sometimes but sometimes it's worth it."

He carried the gannet into a passageway, pausing to look back and say over his shoulder, "Nobody's eating this bird. You pass the word along. Tell them the First Mate said so."

While he was being placed on a table in a room, the young bird suddenly jabbed at his new keeper with his bill. "Thought you might do that," the man told him. "Never saw a sea goose that wouldn't stand up for itself." Reaching behind, he took a sock from a stack in a locker and pulled it over the head and bill. In the dark, weary, lulled by soft words and gentle handling, the bird relaxed.

Now the First Mate occupied himself with figuring how to put a splint on the wing. "Never tried this on a bird before," he said, aloud. "Mended my dog's leg after he was hit by a car and it was good as new when it healed." Opening a drawer, he took out cotton and gauze, and a package of tongue depressors. "These'll have to do," he told the gannet. "Ships like this one don't carry doctors or even have proper sick bays. All we're supposed to do is pick up freight one place and deliver it somewhere else, and keep out of trouble. No accidents allowed!" He smiled as he placed cotton over the wounded area,

47

then gauze to keep it in place and protect the skin and bone from the rub of the wood. When he had put the splints where he wanted them, one on each side of the wing, he secured them with strips of gauze and tape, then stood back to survey his work.

"Not much of a job but the best I can do. You're young so you ought to heal quick if you'll just keep that wing still for a while." He nodded to himself, thinking. "You've had a bad shock and what you need now is time to get over it. Time to be quiet, to be alone. Best thing is to have a box built for you, just big enough for you to stand up in but not to stretch your wings in."

The man moved away once he had removed the sock. "No reason you shouldn't be right as rain by the time we get to the Gulf of Mexico. Bet that's where you're heading. All your kind I've seen down this way in the winter hang around those waters." He lowered his voice. "Tell you a secret. Dad always used to say gannets were the spirits of downed sea-going men, come back to check on their families. When I saw you out there, the first thing I thought about was my kid brother. He's been gone a while now but he was so young . . . just like you."

Being confined was a new experience for the bird but he endured it, as he did the curious members of

48

the crew who gazed upon him in his small prison, sticking fingers through the chicken wire to try to touch or stroke his feathers. He ate the fish which the First Mate caught for him and now and then tested his voice with a guttural "urrah." Most of the time, though, he was silent and watchful, and made no friends.

"You going to give him a name?" someone asked one day when his protector brought his box out on deck to place it in the warm sun. Gulls flew overhead and the gannet watched them intently, his eyes gleaming.

"What's a bird need with a name? I'm turning him loose once we reach the gulf and his wing's strong enough to take him where he wants to go."

A few days later, the mate cut the tape and gauze, removed the splints, and placed the sea goose in a larger box. Now there was room for the wing to be moved about, exercised, tested, and there were as many opinions of its airworthiness as there were men watching.

"We'll see," the mate said, "when the time comes." When it did, the entire ship's crew assembled on deck as the wire was removed from the end of the crate.

"Stand back," the bird's guardian ordered. Then,

turning to the gannet, he coaxed in his quiet voice, "All right, young fellow, you can come out now. It's all yours out here if that wing will let you have it."

At first the bird didn't move, just crouched in the box, eyeing the figures standing about the deck. Round and round in the sky above laughing gulls wheeled and shrieked "ha-ha-haah" cries in their excitement at finding a school of recently hatched fish close beneath the surface. A line of shore-hugging pelicans sailed over the nearby beach where gulf tides lapped at white sands. After a while, the sea goose raised himself to step onto the sun-warmed deck. Bobbing jerkily, he moved to an open space, then cautiously lifted his wings. Several times he repeated this, returning them to his sides afterwards. Next he stretched and flapped them as he had once done while waiting on the high cliffs with the other fledglings for the courage to attempt flight. Now, raising his head high, he rocked back and forth, turning and twisting, before swiveling his eyes to look down under his bill and examine the deck beneath himself. When he finished doing all that was necessary to prepare himself, he suddenly leaped into the air, flailing his wings. Airborne, he managed to clear the ship's railing before going into a long downward glide to the surface of the water.

A cheer went up from the men at his take-off, a
sound that faded as the ship moved on, trailing a
haze of white froth behind. Once again, the bird was
on his own, and for a time he drifted and fed in this
new world he had reached. Winter, with the long
migratory journey over, was a season for rest and
recovery.

SIX

FOR the next three months, the young gannet remained in the Gulf of Mexico, visiting the deep waters, the offshore islands, and the coastal beaches where surface-feeding and sluggish fish could be easily taken.

Often, when far from land and among his own kind, he saw terns which wandered the oceans of the world. Here also were the mystery birds, the sooties and noddies which, after nesting, disappeared to sea though their plumage, not being waterproof, would not allow them to sleep upon the waters as most sea birds did. Their food was caught on the wing, small fish and squid at the surface, and then they were gone again, back into the vast watery wilderness from which they had come.

Here also he found his cousins, the boobies, diving as he did from great heights after food or darting in from a few feet above the water for flying fish which taxied along, their tails beating the surface. Some of the boobies rested upon buoys after a heavy meal, some slept with head under wing while riding the backs of huge seagoing turtles.

During warm days near the shore, he saw skimmers taking their ease, the entire flock facing in the same direction, as they passed the daylight hours on sandbars or dabbled about in the shallows where small sea horses lived, clinging with wrap-around tails to grasses or drifting with the ripples to new pastures. Dusk would send the birds off on nightlong forays for shrimp and small fish that rose from the depths after the sun went down, yelping as they flew like a pack of hound dogs on a trail.

Flocks of cormorants, arriving each morning from their roosts in trees and bushes ashore, formed a great black blot upon the waters, chorusing in piglike grunts as they harvested schools of smelt. Then, facing the wind, they would spread their wings to dry and preen themselves endlessly.

Great brown pelicans, flying with powerful and

slow wingbeat, dived and fished in silent dignity. Only the laughing gulls paid them no respect, sitting upon their heads and leaning to seize their catches as they opened their large bills to empty their pouches of sea water after a dive. White pelicans straggled in and followed their own method of feeding, gathering in groups to thrash the shallows with enormous wings, dipping up the startled fish as they attempted to escape.

From the herring gulls, the gannet learned the trick of escorting ships out of the harbor in order to capture fish disturbed by the sounds and vibrations of engines, as well as retrieve bread or waste tossed overboard. Often he joined the squealing, yelping swarm about small homeward-bound fishing boats to seek the remains thrown out as the fishermen cleaned the day's catch with long filleting knives.

The young bird did well, feeding and resting and growing. Wear was now causing some of his feathers to change appearance, white spots on his tail shafts rubbing off as he swam or dived. He did not molt during this winter but later he would shed the first year dark plumage to gain white upon his head and neck and undersides. After that he would turn patchy and mottled and wear that coat until his feathers turned entirely white, and the tips of his wings black.

At last the days grew longer and the bird's body began to hoard the fat he would need as fuel for the spring migration ahead. A kind of restlessness came over him but he waited. The time was not right.

Washed by the warm, humid, southeast flow of air which crossed the gulf to head into broad northern valleys, the approach of the new season was first taken note of by the birds. There was the departure of the assembly of cormorants who, in taking off from perches, always dropped to the water to wet their tails before climbing uphill into the sky. There were the laughing gulls who now put on black spring hoods and began searching out marshes and islands on which to lay their eggs, in nests which often were no more than shallow depressions in the sand.

Upon the winds from the south came the magnificent frigates, swift and dreaded pirates as well as most graceful of all sea birds, their wings stretching seven feet from tip to tip. Now the booby would have to remain on guard, ever watchful against this huge predator's persecution. Hardly would it dare catch a fish for fear that might bring the waiting robbers swarming down to cuff it about until it surrendered its prize. Should it refuse and hastily swallow the fish, there was the risk of being seized by a tail or leg and turned upside down until it raised again the gulped-down morsel which the bully then snatched, almost before it left the booby's bill.

It was nearly April but still the young gannet waited. Soon the urge would grow strong and send him forth upon the homeward journey. Soon the fever of migration would come over him.

Years before, a terrible hurricane had overtaken a tanker on its way to a gulf port to discharge its cargo, breaking its back and sending it to the bottom only a few miles from shore. There, in a small underwater canyon it had rested, forgotten, its keel tanks still full of oil. With the passing years the metals rusted, slowly, in their salt water bath as the weight of the sea pressed hard upon them. Then, on the first day of this new spring, the casings at last gave way so that gallons of oil belched from under the water to spread a black carpet of tar which was finally pushed all the way to the beaches by winds blowing out of the south. On its way, it brushed the islands, destroying the plant and animal life on which the shore birds fed. Birds caught in the sticky mass were helpless, and as the days went by there were hundreds of them trapped in rafts of the oil and finally washed ashore, some dead, some dying, all unable to fly.

It had been the young straggler's habit all winter

to spend some time among the gulls, loons, and grebes in the shallows after a few weeks on the deep water. He arrived on the day following the disaster, when the coast was awash with black filth and, as usual, set about plunging for fish along with other birds. In only a short time, he was streaked with oil and barely managed to limp onto the beach where he rested, unable to become airborne because of the coating on his feathers.

In order to save the birds, once news of the disaster reached them, an army of people descended upon the shores to gather up what victims they could find and take them to treatment centers in the town. Some could be easily cleaned and then released, little the worse for their experience. Others were dead or nearly so from having preened their feathers of oil which, carried into their bodies, proved deadly when digested. Some died of the exposure they had suffered, some of starvation, being unable to move about and capture food.

"There's one! there's one!" a girl shouted, running along the blackened sands to where the young sea goose crouched, at the edge of the oil-laden tide lapping the beach.

Behind her came a boy crying out, loudly, "Come on, Grandma. We've found one!"

"Why, I believe it's a gannet," the woman said when she caught up with the children and stood beside them to gaze down at the stricken bird. "They can be real rough customers, I know, when they're frightened. I'd almost rather tackle a swan. They, at least, get friendly after a while."

"But we can't just leave it here," the girl insisted. "See how it's looking at us, as if it wants us to help it."

"Sure," the boy agreed, dancing about in excitement, "we found it so we ought to save it. It's our bird now."

The girl squealed in annoyance. "It isn't *our* bird. I found it so it's mine. You're always butting in. . . ."

The woman settled the matter quickly. "You can each claim half if you want to although all you'll have will be a dead bird if you stand here arguing." She took a large beach towel she was carrying and threw it over the bird's head, pinning it loosely at the neck. "They're easier to manage when they're in the dark," she told the children. "Now, hand me the basket."

They carried the gannet to the car and when they reached home, took the basket into the kitchen and set it on the table. "We'd better get busy," the woman said. "I think we have a good chance of saving this bird since it's only lightly oiled. Probably hasn't even lost its waterfproofing."

"Lucky you were over in England when the oil got all over the beaches there," the girl said. "If you hadn't been, I guess you wouldn't know what to do now."

"Lucky we're here for our Easter vacation," her brother piped up, "or Grandma wouldn't have us to help her."

The oven was turned on and a package of cotton wool laid out. The children pushed closer to the basket in which the gannet rested, the towel still over its head.

"What do we do first?" the girl asked. "Clean its feathers?"

The grandmother shook her head. "No, not until tomorrow. First we see that it's warm and dry, and then that it's fed."

She pulled off wads of the raw cotton and tucked them under the bird's wings, then unrolled a large sheet of it and wrapped this about its body. After that, she removed the towel.

"Don't either of you get too near," she cautioned. "It's only a young bird but its bill can be dangerous."

The sea goose stared back at the humans, not too alarmed since once before he had been handled, had become used to the sound of voices. However, he did open his bill in warning.

"That's good," the woman said. "It'll be easier to feed than those you have to coax and force to open up. Now, let's let it warm up and steam a while so its feathers can dry out. You'll see it brighten up soon."

She sent the children to the market for fish, and sat down on the other side of the room to study entries in a notebook. Finally, laying the booklet aside, she went to the refrigerator, removed a small bottle, and poured cream from it into a large spoon. As she approached, the bird opened his bill again, threatening, and with a quick thrust, she poured the liquid down his throat. "That'll help take care of what oil you may have swallowed," she told him.

Next, she went into the pantry and opened one drawer after another quietly, making sure not to alarm the gannet with sudden movements or loud noises, until she found the heavy pair of gloves she was looking for. All the while she continued talking to him, soothingly, softly. "You gannets were the worst over there in England. You bit the hand that fed you every time you got the chance."

When the girl and boy returned with a sack full of fish, they both tried to tell the story at once. "The man at the market didn't have any herring like you said but he told us . . ."

". . . we should go to the bait store," the boy cut in. "We did and when we told that man what the fish was for, he gave us . . ."

". . . some whole fish," the girl continued, taking the words right out of the boy's mouth. "I can't remember the name but it began with an *m*, I think. He said they were oily trash fish that people around here don't eat but they'd be . . ."

". . . good enough for a bird," the boy said quickly, managing to get in the last word.

Their grandmother nodded. "Menhaden." She cut one in thin slices, put on the heavy gloves, and approached the sea goose. Again his bill gaped, warning her, and she dropped the morsels in, one at a time, then stepped back. After she had turned the oven down, she led the children out of the room and closed the door behind them. "Let the bird rest now. Later on we'll see if it wants to do some stretching, maybe even try to work its wings. And tomorrow we'll do our best to clean it up. If it manages to get through the next forty-eight hours, there's a good chance it may live to fly again some day."

SEVEN

THE newspapers of the area carried stories and pictures of the disaster and, after reading them, the woman told her grandchildren, "They're going to start using detergents today so what bird life the oil didn't destroy, the chemicals will. What it doesn't say here is how that stuff burns the birds and wipes out the plankton, and once that's gone, it's going to be a long time before this place recovers."

She sighed. "Well, at least we saved your gannet before they began turning the gulf waters into a giant dishpan full of suds. They'll be dumping hundreds of gallons into the water and whipping it up with boat propellers all day long."

Standing up, she beckoned to the boy and girl. "Time now to start cleaning up your bird since it got through the night all right."

Once again she draped a towel over the gannet's head, and again he relaxed in the darkness, making no attempt to fight off the hands working on his feathers. The woman talked while she worked, in low soft tones so as not to distress him. "In England some people used soap to try to get the oil off, others used lard to melt the tar. I remembered how my father cleaned grease from his sheep's wool back on our ranch in Texas by using a kind of sand and clay he dug up out of the earth, so I tried that on feathers and it worked. I bought a mixture like it at the drug store yesterday, just in case we found a bird." She rubbed the chalky shampoo into the gannet's plumage, gently.

The children crowded close, watching her every move. "Can we help?" they asked, eager to get their hands on the bird, to stroke it, to enjoy their new possession.

"Not today. I'll wash this off later this evening, then do the whole thing over again day after tomorrow. You can help then."

It took a few days of this routine, rubbing the chalk in, letting it remain during the day, then rinsing it off with warm water, to remove all the oil. All the while the bird was kept comfortable in the kitchen, dried thoroughly with a hair dryer after each treatment, and allowed to exercise his wings. As the days went by he began to let them know when he was hungry by opening and closing his bill, and began accepting the offered fish more politely. Soon he was eating a half-dozen or so herring or menhaden at a meal, fussy about but one thing, that they be presented to him head first.

When the children's parents arrived to gather them up and head for their inland home, five hundred miles north of the Gulf of Mexico, they were taken immediately to see the gannet.

"It's ours!" the boy cried, jumping about in delight.

"Stop jumping!" the girl told him. "You'll scare it. You know what Grandma told you about keeping your voice down and moving slowly."

"She told you too," the boy said, "and sometimes you forget."

Ignoring him, his sister turned to the parents. "It's half mine and half his but I saw it first. Can we take it home?"

"That bill looks dangerous to me," her father

said. "How do you know it won't jab you when you get near?"

The boy hopped up and down again, impatiently. " 'Cause we don't get that near. Grandma says it isn't used to being petted so we mustn't put our hands on it."

There was a long conference among the three adults before it was decided the gannet would be put in a large wicker cage the grandmother had in her attic, and transported along with the luggage in the back of the station wagon. "When it gets good and strong again," the boy said, "we'll let it loose so it can fly back to wherever it lives."

"Oh, no, we won't," his sister cried. "I'm going to keep it forever and ever for a pet. Grandma said we each owned half but as long as I discovered it, I get to say which half is mine. I choose the half with its legs so if it never flies again, it can't go anywhere unless I say so."

"When will they stop arguing over everything?" their mother asked, and the older woman smiled as she told her, "I remember when you and your brother were that age . . . you acted just the same way. Don't worry, they'll get over it when they're older."

She turned to bid the children good-by, telling

them, "You must remember there is a chance that when the bird gets completely well it still won't be able to float on water anymore. Nobody knows why or what to do about it but for a sea bird like this it could mean the end of its old way of life. A lot of those birds they thought they'd saved in England, died at sea soon after they turned them loose." Seeing the look on the boy's face, she hurried to add, "Of course there's just as good a chance it won't happen to your bird, or if it does, the gannet will get over it after a time."

Waving when they were in the car and ready to go, she called out, "Now just be sure to put the bird in a pen large enough for it to exercise its wings and move about. And don't forget to feed it the fish head first!"

The family headed north on the highway beside the Mississippi River which separated the eastern third from the rest of the country. It took them from early morning until after sundown to reach home, four hundred and fifty miles due north of the gulf.

"Grandma said when a bird gets sick or hurt, it gets nervous on account of it doesn't believe it'll ever be able to do things like it used to," the boy told his father as they built an enclosure in the back yard. "Maybe once our bird gets used to its new home, it'll stop being nervous. I sure wish it'd let me pet it. I sure wish it'd get to be my friend."

The gannet, however, didn't make friends during the time he lived in the pen. He stared back at the crowds of children who came to look at him, reacting only when the boy brought the fish for his dinner. Awkward and uncomfortable on land, he spent a lot of time between feedings in testings his wings. His cage wasn't large enough for him to become airborne within its wire walls, but sometimes he would wind himself up in preparation for a take-off anyway. Raising his head, looking cross-eyed down at the ground, he would bound into the air and almost at once crash against a barrier, repeating his actions over and over again as if there was a need to convince himself it was hopeless.

Early one afternoon when he had been there several weeks, as a late spring storm was blowing up and bringing wind and rain with it, the boy came to the pen and, after feeding the bird, leaned his head against the wire.

"She's the one that said she wanted to keep you forever for a pet, remember? But you haven't seen her out here for a long time now, have you? She never goes to the store to get your fish or comes out and feeds you so I don't see why she's got any right to her half anymore." He opened the gate a crack. "You heard her say her half had your feet on it, didn't you? Well, that makes the half with your wings on it mine. I think sea birds ought to be at sea instead of a thousand miles away and it makes me feel awful when I watch you doing your best to get out of here and go home." He shook his head sadly. "You're never going to be my friend. Birds like you don't need friends like me, I guess." He swung the door open, hooked it there, then stood back against a tree, out of the way.

It didn't take the bird long to venture out of the pen. Bobbing and stumbling along on his web-feet, he found himself suddenly free of restraint for the first time since landing on the oil-covered offshore waters of the gulf. Turning to face a rising wind, he hesitated only briefly before hurling himself into the air. For a moment he seemed to hang there, uncertain, but then, with much thrashing and beating, he began to rise. His long narrow wings, designed to ride wind gusts, carried him aloft and he was on his way to seek a good updraft under a cumulus cloud which even now was developing into a thunderhead. Later, the boy wrote his grandmother that the gannet had taken time to thank him before leaving, telling her how it had uttered a loud "urrah" while making a wide circle overhead before disappearing into the turbulence above.

Now that he was free and in the air again, the sea goose was drawn to the east, the direction of the far-off ocean. Although the migrating season was growing late, the homing drive remained strong within him. By now most of his kind would have reached the northern feeding grounds at the rim of the deep sea.

Below lay unfamiliar terrain, with no clues to show him the right track. At first he limped through the sky, his wings unaccustomed to use after his long inactivity. Carried like a swimmer in these air currents, he was fortunate in being helped along by a better-than-fair tail wind, traveling directly in the path of the storm. His hollow bones and feathers were the right combination of lightness and toughness so, though out of practice and not as strong as he had been before, he was able to remain aloft without discomfort. Then, sighting a lake, he dropped low, intending to seek food but as his keen eyes searched the area for favorable signs, he heard a sudden explosion. This caused him to climb the sky again rapidly, turning on that extra speed he held in reserve for escape from danger. Below, two wild geese which had been feeding by standing on

71

their heads in the water to reach plants beneath the surface, honked and clattered noisily as they rose in the air, and in a small stand of trees near the lake, a man slunk away quickly after hiding his gun in a hollow tree. There would be no illegal bird for his dinner tonight, its body grown fat through long winter months of feeding in the great coastal marshes to the south.

Two hours later, the gannet again swept low upon sighting a river. Having no other flight plan than to reach the sea, this river valley offered him something to follow since it tended in the right direction. First, however, he must feed and rest.

In the center of the river was a small island and upon its shore he could see various waterfowl, interrupting their leisurely spring flights to refuel and gather strength for the long journeys ahead of them. Just as he had fed beside shore birds in the shoals of the gulf, the gannet now prepared to join and feed along with these birds, on tidbits to be discovered in the plant growth at the water's edge as well as fish that might inhabit the river.

Hardly had he touched water beside the geese and ducks there in the shallows than a large net, fired downwind by explosive rockets from the muddy shore, shot up and over the entire gathering, its mesh trapping them as they fed. Quacking shrilly, some of the ducks attempted to take flight as the snare descended, their wings beating rapidly. This, however, only led them to pile one upon another in a scramble of feathers. The geese gabbled frantically and the young gannet, caught also, joined the chorus with a loud protesting bark.

EIGHT

Two men, standing on the river's edge, looked over their catch. "Say, there's a real prize," the older one pointed out. "A sea bird. Hardly ever find one this far inland unless it's been blown in by a storm." He frowned. "No storms like that been around lately that I've read about."

"Looks like a cross between a gull and a goose, doesn't it?" his young helper said.

"Matter of fact it's called a sea goose by some, though it's known as a gannet to most folks. This one looks young, tired too judging by the way he came in for a landing. Could be hungry. Maybe that's what brought him down."

"He'll find plenty around to feed on once we get him banded and turn him loose. Those honkers sure were stuffing themselves before he arrived."

"Uh, uh," the first man, a federal agent, said. "You won't find him eating grass or shoots. Might catch some fish in the river if he's lucky but if he's headed back to sea the way I think he is, he'll never make it. Not enough of his kind of food to be had between here and there. He'll need plenty to keep up his strength on a trip like that."

They set up a table which had open-ended, bucket-shaped metal containers inserted at regular intervals into its surface. On another they placed a box of numbered leg bands, a tool to use in attaching them, brightly colored neck bands for special project marking, a scale for weighing, tape for measuring, and a notebook to use in recording the gathered information.

"Want the sea bird first?" the young assistant asked before raising a corner of the net.

The conservationist thought it over. "No, let's leave him for last. I have the beginning of an idea that might be the answer as far as he's concerned. I'll be figuring on it while we take care of the others."

They went to work on the geese and ducks, patiently loosening the entangling mesh of the net in

75

removing each bird, then placing the bird upside down in one of the metal pails so that its head and neck appeared out the smaller end which was below the table top. In this way, the leg was in a convenient position to be banded.

"Think I like working on these big ones better'n the swallows and warblers and sparrows we got in those mist nets we strung between the trees yesterday," the helper said. "Always worry for fear I might be too rough with the little ones. Their legs aren't any bigger than matchsticks."

The bird bander nodded. "I know what you mean. Took me a while to get over that feeling when I was first starting out too. The big ones are really the important ones this trip and the reason why I'm here. Everyone of them is a straggler and it's their habits I want to find out about. Never band one that I don't try guessing why he fell behind or what made her end up five hundred miles from where she ought to be this time of year according to our best information. Blue geese stay late in the marshes, for instance, and then they fly north as if demons were on their tails, humping it all the way so they'll get to their breeding grounds in time. Now, what made this one," he pointed to one standing on its head in the bucket, "stay even later down there on the gulf and just mosey along now in no hurry at all? And why do you suppose that wood duck's here now, and what's he doing in a place like this? He ought to be keeping a wedding date somewhere because after the first of June, he's due to go off with a crowd of his buddies to some hide-out and molt for a couple of weeks. What could have happened to his time schedule this year?"

At dusk they released the geese, finished with them, and the birds flew off, headed for a brief summer on islands in half-frozen northern bays. Two black ducks, wild and wary, took off in haste, their pale wing linings flashing silver as they flew. The wood duck departed in a leisurely fashion, showing no particular hurry to remove himself from the area.

Now only the gannet was left in the net. "You decided what to do with him?" the young worker asked. "If you want, I could keep him until he's rested up a bit, then turn him loose, seeing that you've got to start for home tonight."

"Thanks, anyway," his boss told him, "but I've made up my mind. What you can do is to get me those cans of sardines we didn't eat. After we band him, I'm going to put the same drug in them that I use when I set out bait for a flock I have to move from one state to another. It's harmless but if he takes it, it'll knock him out and I can carry him along with me when I leave. He can rest up during the trip and when I get home I'll be able to get fresh fish and feed him good before I turn him loose. It's only a hundred miles to the sea from there and he ought to be able to get back where he belongs by himself." He shook his head. "He'd never make it from here, with hundreds of miles to fly, tired as he is. Probably wouldn't even have the strength for a take-off. What he needs is fuel to travel on and only proper food can give him that."

It surprised him to see the gannet gape when the fish was offered, as if he were used to being fed. "I've been in this work a long time," he mused, "but seems I'll never learn you can't be sure of anything. Here I was expecting him to take off my finger with that bill of his if I got careless and instead, he's meek as a lamb with an appetite like a horse's."

After the drug took effect, he gently picked up the gannet and laid him on a blanket spread out on the back of the car. Then he covered him with a net as a precaution against a sudden awakening.

"I'll let you know if we ever hear any more about this one," he told the young helper in farewell. "I like to band a young one like this because he'll carry it longer and have an even better chance of being caught again. Who knows, maybe someday someone will send in the information on his band and tell us where and when they found him, and we'll be able to write another chapter on his life. Wish I had some way of knowing what it's been like for him up to now."

Four days later, the gannet was in the air again, rested and fed. The bird bander had waited for the right kind of day, and driven to the right spot before releasing him.

"I drove you through the mountains, my friend, so you won't have to worry about getting over them," he told the bird in farewell. "Just follow your bill now and you ought to be back in familiar territory by nightfall."

High on a steep hill, the carrying cage was opened and the gannet, stumbling out, met the rush of wind which rose to clear the heights. Flinging himself into it, he soared upward, searching immediately for a clue to which path he should take. Again, the pull to the east was strong, the pull of an ocean still too far away to be seen.

All day long the bird flew in the warm air ascending from the broad coastal plains below. Whereas at sea he would have traveled low, cruising just above the water, now he flew high, ignoring rivers and lakes, along an unmarked yet true course. When, at last, the coast came in view, he left the unfamiliar altitude and began a long downward glide that took him, finally, over a broad beach on which breakers curled and crashed. Beyond, where great rolling swells moved forward, the sea goose dropped low to skim the surface. Suddenly, he crashed into a slope of water and emerged as it passed to float high upon the trough between it and the next swell.

Had he been able to see him now, the boy back in the middle of the country could have rested easy. The bird had fully recovered from his oil bath. He could float upon the water as he had floated before, still secure in his waterproofing.

Again and again the gannet bathed, then flapped his wings, preened by stroking with his bill to adjust his plumage, gaped, shook his head and feathers, preened again, and bathed once more.

By nightfall he had reached the area where, months before, killer whales had raided the gannet flock and left the young bird to continue his south-ward journey alone. Now he rested close to the island's shore where May violets, June berries, and beach plums grew on the dunes, where sparrows and swallows fed in the salty marshes along with retiring

bitterns and shy yellowlegs. Here grackle and lark strolled the sands in their daily hunt for food.

Late-lingering terns plummeted headlong into the waters beside him as he plunged and fished the next day. The northward-flowing "river" of sea birds had rolled above this way station almost a month before so now the scattering of migrants were mainly pre-breeders, young and inexperienced, finding their way alone after some untoward happening separated them from the flock to which they belonged. Here too were those which had found a river's mouth, a bay, or an inlet irresistible and had left the beaten path to investigate. Now they straggled back to home waters with little but an inner pull to direct them.

Riding the air currents on his way to the feeding grounds at the edge of the deep sea, the young gannet swept confidently above the water on his strong wings. Months before, he had departed, an untried youngster. He returned now with thousands of miles of travel behind him, educated in the geography to fit his needs, skillful at finding his food supply, wise in recognizing predators, fully aware how to turn wind and wave to his own advantage.

The waters of the continental shelf were boiling with activity when at last he arrived there. Swift, long-winged kittiwakes dived by the thousands, swimming underwater to capture their prey. Skuas screamed and fought, attacked and robbed. Black dovekies busily searched for plankton, and fulmars trailed small fish moving just beneath the surface. The smoke of spray as well as squeals, screams, yelps, and squawks filled the air as the meadows of the sea gave up their treasure.

A straggler no longer, his great adventure behind him now, the sea goose joined his brothers as they circled lower in a mass attack on a vast school of herring. Then, as the fish swam deeper, the flock rose higher in the air, each bird selecting a target before stalling suddenly, neatly folding wings and then plunging steeply far below the surface to swim up and strike from below. Hour after hour they fed, a few mature gannets, great white birds with black-tipped wings and golden heads among the hundreds of one and two and three-year-olds in spangled or spotted or mottled plumage. One day these too would return to the northern cliffs to join the colony, to mate and nest, and so continue the story of the gannet, sometimes called sea goose.

Men leaned on the railing of a fishing boat a half mile away and cupped hands over eyes to lessen the glare on the sea as they watched.

"There they are, taking our fish again," one said, nodding toward the feathered divers. "What a life! Nothing to do but eat and sleep, all summer long. Then, when it gets cold, they take a nice easy trip south for the winter."

"Sure sounds good to me," another agreed. "No worries, no troubles. Think I'd like to come back next time as a sea bird."

One of the men rubbed his chin thoughtfully, his eyes on the salt spray shooting high in the air. "Uh, uh," he said finally, "count me out on that. All those birds do is go through the same old routine day after day, year after year. It's not knowing what's going to happen next that makes life interesting far as I'm concerned." He shook his head as he watched the blizzard of birds hovering over the water. "What do they know about taking a risk or facing up to danger? Why, I'll bet you there's not a single one of them out there that ever had an adventure worth telling about."